ON THE BALL

FIRST MATCH

FRANCES MACKAY

The fifth book in the series
ON THE BALL

It was the week before the first match.

Mr Jones had called a team meeting.

Matt had left to go to another school and Ben really missed him.

'We need another player for Saturday's match,' said Mr Jones.

'I have put Paul on the team and made Ali the second sub.'

Ben found it hard to listen to Mr Jones.

He was thinking about Matt and how much the team will miss him.

'Ben, are you listening?' asked Mr Jones.

'Umm ... yes, Mr Jones,' said Ben.

'Good, because we all need to be very clear about what is happening on Saturday. Good luck, team. We can win, I know we can!' said Mr Jones.

Ben trained hard all week.

He skipped for ten minutes and did ten star jumps before breakfast.

He ran to school and back every day.

He practised his dribbling skills every break-time.

He ran up and down the playground ten times and played a game every lunchtime.

He practised ball skills every day after school.

Ben felt he was ready for his first match.

He was looking forward to Saturday. But he wasn't looking forward to playing in his PE kit.

'We won't look like a proper team without a football strip,' he said to his mum.

'I'm sure you'll still do well,' his mum replied. 'It's the team that counts.'

Ben wasn't so sure. How would they work as a team without their strip?

Saturday finally arrived.

The sun was shining brightly into Ben's bedroom.

'At least it's not raining,' thought Ben, as he got dressed.

'Maybe it won't be so bad, after all.'

Ben's mum drove him to the match.

Ben was surprised to see so many children from school who had come to watch.

'Good luck, Ben,' yelled Sam, as he waved to him from the edge of the pitch.

Ben waved back and walked into the changing rooms.

Ben looked around the room.

All the players were in white, but none of the T-shirts and shorts were the same.

Some T-shirts had writing on them.

Some of the shorts were long and baggy, and others were short.

Everyone had different coloured socks on.

'What a scruffy lot we look,' thought Ben.

'Well, this is it, everyone,' said Mr Jones. 'Our very first match. All I ask is that you try your best and enjoy it.'

The team got into line and ran out onto the pitch.

The players from Brent Park Primary were already there.

They looked really cool in their matching blue football strip.

'Hey, look at them!' Ben heard a Brent Park supporter call out. 'They look a right bunch. Don't even look like a proper team. We'll beat 'em, no problem.'

Some of the other Brent Park supporters started to snigger.

Ben looked at Dan and Chris.

'They're right, you know,' said Dan. 'I don't feel like I'm a part of a proper team without our strip.'

Brent Park won the toss and they quickly pushed forward, making some very good passes.

Ben's team just couldn't keep up.

Their tackles failed one after the other and, in no time at all, Brent Park had taken a shot at goal and scored – only two minutes into the first half.

'Yes!!' yelled the Brent Park supporters.

'Come on, team. Don't let it get you down,' yelled Sam.

Ben kicked off and Dan crossed the ball to Chris.

Chris was making good progress down the pitch when suddenly a Brent Park defender tackled him and took control of the ball.

Brent Park were off again.

Ben and Dan couldn't keep up.

Then David put on an extra spurt and raced forward.

He was just about to make a tackle when he yelled out and suddenly fell to the ground.

The referee blew his whistle.

'What happened, David?' asked Ben.

'It's my ankle. I twisted it when I tried to tackle,' said David.

David limped off and Ramjeet came on.

Brent Park continued to dominate the first half.

Ben's team just couldn't seem to do anything right.

Then Ben got the ball.

'Come on, Ben, you can do it!' shouted Ben's mum from the sidelines.

Ben ran down the pitch, feeling the wind on his face.

'I can do this, I know I can,' he said to himself.

He dribbled safely away from a Brent Park defender and lined himself up for the shot.

He could see their keeper moving to his right, so Ben aimed for the other side and kicked the ball hard.

'PLEASE go in,' Ben whispered to himself, as he watched the ball head towards the goal.

The ball flew into the air.

It was high.

'Oh no!' said Ben.

The ball was too high and it clipped the top of the bar and veered off.

No goal.

Ben hung his head and walked back up the pitch.

'We've lost,' he thought, as he made his way back.

At half-time Mr Jones spoke to the team.

The score was 3-0 to Brent Park.

'What's up with you lot? I can't believe you're the same team I see at practice each week,' said Mr Jones.

'The Brent Park supporters all laughed at us when we came on the pitch,' said Ben.

'We don't feel like a proper team without our strip,' said Dan.

'That's not what makes a team,' said Mr Jones. 'Brent Park might look the part, but we've got what it really takes. Besides, look who's here!'

'Matt! What're you doing here?' asked Ben.

'Mr Jones told us that Matt was coming down today,' said Sim.

'He did?' said Ben.

Then he remembered he hadn't been listening to Mr Jones at the team meeting that week.

'This is great!' he said, beaming.

'Yes, I've agreed that Matt can play in the second half,' said Mr Jones. 'He's a good player, we all know that, but he isn't the only one. Look around you. Look at all the other good players we have. Think about all the hard training we've done. Are you really going to let a football strip get in the way of being the best team?'

Everyone looked at each other.

They knew they had to forget about the first half and start playing as a team.

'Come on, we can do it,' said Dan.

It was hard on Paul, as he had to come off so Matt could take his place, but he was happy to see the team working together again.

Brent Park didn't know what had hit them in the second half – it was like playing against a different team.

Ben kicked off and sent a cross-field pass to Dan, who picked out Sim on the wing.

Sim flew like the wind up the left, with a long cross into the box where Matt was waiting.

Quick as a flash, Matt knocked it into the bottom corner and the first goal was scored.

'Way to go, Matt!' yelled Sam from the sidelines.

The Brent Park players were shaken. They hadn't expected that!

They soon took control again and their forwards moved swiftly downfield to have a shot at goal.

Tom was ready. He made a brilliant dive and tipped the ball over the bar.

No goal!

'Well done, Tom,' yelled Ben's mum.

Within minutes, Brent Park were in a position to score again.

Tom was ready and waiting.

He never took his eye off the ball.

The Brent Park player took aim.

The ball flew fast and high to the right hand corner, but Tom was even faster.

He dived with all his might and caught the ball.

No goal.

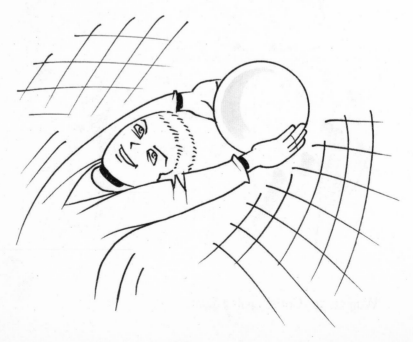

Ben's team were really fired up now.

They felt like a proper team at last, and they played harder than they'd ever played before.

Chris even scored a volley from the halfway line.

The supporters went wild.

'Way to go, Chris!' yelled Sam.

With only ten minutes to go, Ben's team picked up the pace even further.

After a free kick, Dan made a perfect cross to Matt, who skilfully found the net for his second goal.

Five minutes to go.

Oliver made a sound tackle to regain the ball.

He passed it to Ramjeet, who raced down the field.

He could see Ben, who was well-placed in front of goal.

Matt received the pass from Ramjeet and made a perfect cross to Ben.

'This is it!' thought Ben. 'I'll do it this time!'

He took careful aim and kicked the ball.

Time seemed to stand still.

Ben held his breath as he watched the ball fly through the air.

It found the net.

Goal!

The supporters went wild again.

Ben's team had won by one goal.

'We won, we really won!' yelled Ben, as he raced up to Matt.

Everyone jumped around, hugging each other.

Mr Jones couldn't stop grinning.

Ben's mum ran over.

'I knew you could do it – with or without a proper football strip,' she said, as she gave him a hug.

It was true. The strip didn't matter.

What really mattered was working as a team.

'And I have more good news for you,' his mum said. 'Matt's parents have agreed to let Matt stay with us until the end of the school year.'

'Yes!' said Ben, as he punched the air with his fists. 'This is the best day yet!'

As they walked off, Matt saw something.

He thought he saw the man who had tried to win their goal shoot competition at the supermarket.

The man wasn't looking very happy.

'That's strange. What's he doing here?' thought Matt.

The next book in the series is:

THE CHAMPIONS

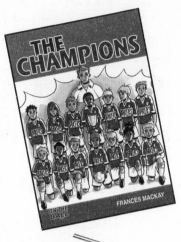

HOW MANY HAVE YOU READ?